The Starf

By Cynthia Rider

Illustrations by Jon Stuart

OXFORD

UNIVERSITY PRESS

In this story ...

💬 **TALK**

- Introduce children to the characters in this story: Max, Cat, Ant and Tiger.
- Point to the words that represent the characters' names and say each of the names together. Children will meet these words in the story.

Max

Cat

Ant

Tiger

The four friends have special watches. When they push the buttons on their watches they can shrink to micro-size, like this …

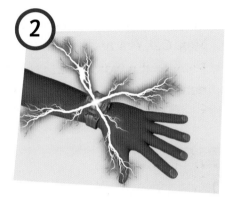

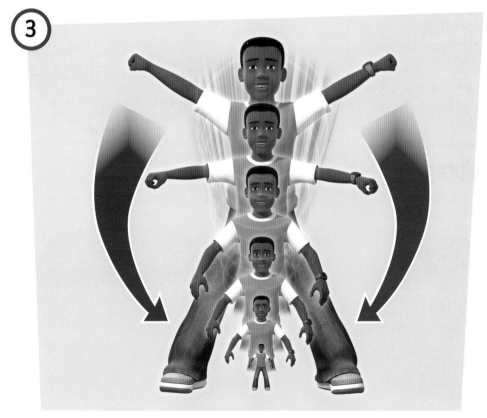

They become tiny and can have amazing adventures!

📖 READ

Max, Cat, Ant and Tiger were at the beach with Tiger's mum and dad. The four friends had set off to explore the rock pools. They were looking for shells and crabs. Max saw a small cave in the rocks.

"Let's shrink and explore this cave!" he said.

👥 ACTIVITY

- Read out the following sentence: *A fish is in the rock pool near the weed.* Ask children to sound-talk the word *near* (i.e. near becomes n-ear).
- Then ask children to blend the sounds together and say the word (i.e. n-ear becomes near).
- Ask children to tell you which letter they would need to change in the word *near* to make the word *hear*.

✳ Tip

See the inside back cover for more guidance on sounds.

rock pool

crab

4

📖 READ

They all pushed the buttons on their watches to shrink to micro-size.

The four friends crept into the cave. As they went further in, the cave grew darker, damp and stuffy.

Cat wanted to get back into the fresh air but Max wanted to explore a tunnel.

💬 TALK

- Talk about the cave. Ask children to think of words to describe how the cave might smell. Use this as an opportunity to extend their vocabulary (e.g. musty, salty).

👥 ACTIVITY

- Point to the word *down* on the page and ask children to sound-talk it (i.e. down becomes d-ow-n).
- Then ask children to blend the sounds together and say the word (i.e. d-ow-n becomes down).

Can we go back? I need air.

📖 READ

Tiger turned on the light on his watch so they could all see.

Just then, Max saw a starfish in the tunnel.

"Oh dear!" said Ant. "The starfish is too far from the water in here. We need to get it back to the rock pool."

💬 TALK

- Tell children some starfish facts:
  - Starfish cannot swim. They crawl and climb.
  - Starfish have 'arms'.
  - Most starfish have five arms but some have as many as twelve!
  - Starfish breathe through their feet.

👥 ACTIVITY

- Read out the following sentence: *The light from Tiger's watch points at the starfish.* Ask children to sound-talk the word *point* (i.e. point becomes p-oi-n-t). Ask children to use a finger to point as they say each sound.

Wow! Look at the starfish!

READ

"We need something to put the starfish on," said Max. "Then we can drag it out to the rock pool."

Cat pulled at some litter that was stuck under a rock. "Will this sweet wrapper do?" she asked.

"I'm sure it will," said Max. "Let's lift the starfish on to it."

ACTIVITY

- Point to the word *litter* on the page and ask children to sound-talk it (i.e. litter becomes l-i-tt-er).

- Ask children to make the last sound in the word *litter* (i.e. the /er/ sound). Can children think of other words that end in the /er/ sound (e.g. butter, mother)?

- Read out the following sentences and ask children to say the missing words. Both of the words end in the /er/ sound:

  ○ *It is cold at the seaside in the …* (winter)

  ○ *It is hot at the seaside in the …* (summer)

- Then ask children to write the word *winter*. Children could use magnetic letters, a whiteboard or pencil and paper to write.

📖 READ

The children pulled the starfish back down the tunnel. It was hard work.

Suddenly, Ant stopped. He thought he heard something. "It sounds like the sea," he said.

"Quick!" cried Max. "The tide must be coming in."

💬 TALK

- Ask children to think of words to describe the sounds that Ant heard. Use this as an opportunity to extend their vocabulary (e.g. crash, roar).

👥 ACTIVITY

- Point to the word *hear* on the page and ask children to sound-talk it (i.e. hear becomes h-ear).
- Then ask children to write the sentence: *The starfish is near the pool.*

⭐ Tip

Encourage children to sound-talk the words before writing.

Cat got her
hair wet!

📖 READ

With one last heave, they got the starfish out of the cave and into the water. Cat was the last to let go. The starfish wriggled and splashed her.

"Urgh! I'm soaked!" she cried.

Sea water splashed around them.

"Time to grow back to normal size!" said Max. So they all pushed the buttons on their watches.

💬 TALK

- Ask children how they thought the starfish might have felt when it reached the water.

👥 ACTIVITY

- Point to the word *her* on the page and ask children to sound-talk it (i.e. her becomes h-er).
- Then ask children to blend the sounds together and say the word (i.e. h-er becomes her).

READ

Max, Cat, Ant and Tiger walked back down the beach to find Tiger's mum and dad.

"There you all are!" said Tiger's dad. "We are just going to get fish and chips. Would you like some?"

"Yes, please!" said the four friends.

 TALK

- Talk about things you can do at the beach.